# Life's Answers
## (And Much, Much More)

*by*
*Schulz*

**CollinsPublishersSanFrancisco**
*A Division of* HarperCollins*Publishers*

# The
# Secret Of
# Life

# The Secret Of Life

# The Secret Of Life

# Live
# And
# Learn

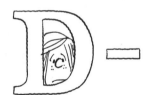 -

# Tomorrow
# Is
# Another Day

**A Packaged Goods Incorporated Book**
**First published 1996 by Collins Publishers San Francisco**
**1160 Battery Street, San Francisco, CA 94111-1213**
**http://www.harpercollins.com**
**Conceived and produced by Packaged Goods Incorporated**
**276 Fifth Avenue, New York, NY 10001**
**A Quarto Company**

**Library of Congress Cataloging-in-Publication Data**
**Schulz, Charles M.**
**[Peanuts. Selections]**
**Life's answers (and much, much more) / by Schulz.**
**p.        cm.**
**ISBN 0-00-225178-7**
**I. Title**
**PN6728.P4S3246          1996**
**741.5'973—dc20          96-8338**
**CIP**

**Printed in Hong Kong**

**1  3  5  7  9  10  8  6  4  2**